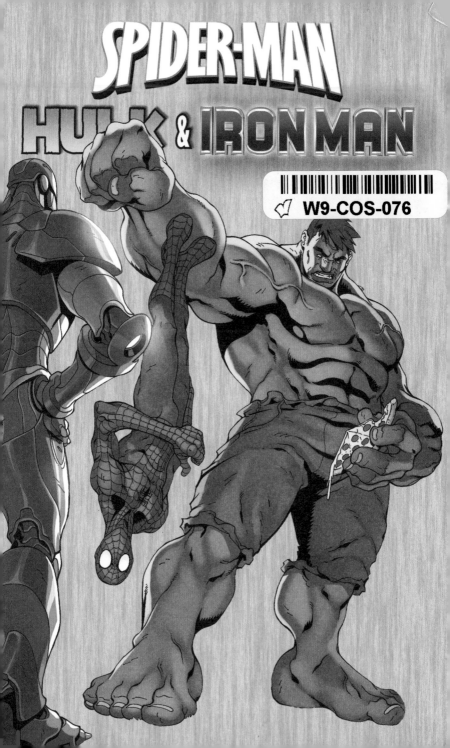

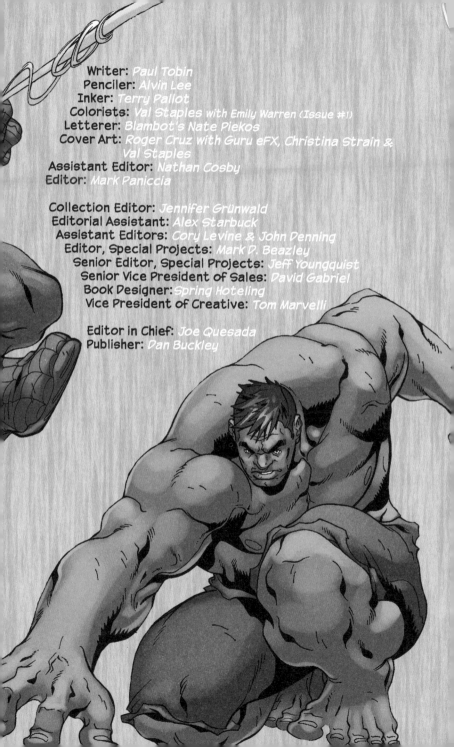

Writer: Paul Tobin
Penciler: Alvin Lee
Inker: Terry Pallot
Colorists: Val Staples with Emily Warren (Issue #1)
Letterer: Blambot's Nate Piekos
Cover Art: Roger Cruz with Guru eFX, Christina Strain &
Val Staples
Assistant Editor: Nathan Cosby
Editor: Mark Paniccia

Collection Editor: Jennifer Grünwald
Editorial Assistant: Alex Starbuck
Assistant Editors: Cory Levine & John Denning
Editor, Special Projects: Mark D. Beazley
Senior Editor, Special Projects: Jeff Youngquist
Senior Vice President of Sales: David Gabriel
Book Designer: Spring Hoteling
Vice President of Creative: Tom Marvelli

Editor in Chief: Joe Quesada
Publisher: Dan Buckley

#1

BITTEN BY AN IRRADIATED SPIDER, WHICH GRANTED HIM INCREDIBLE ABILITIES, PETER PARKER LEARNED THE ALL-IMPORTANT LESSON, THAT WITH GREAT POWER THERE MUST ALSO COME GREAT RESPONSIBILITY. AND SO HE BECAME THE AMAZING

SPIDER-MAN

CAUGHT IN A BLAST OF GAMMA-IRRADIATION, BRILLIANT SCIENTIST BRUCE BANNER HAS BEEN TRANSFORMED INTO THE LIVING ENGINE OF DESTRUCTION KNOWN AS THE

HULK

BILLIONAIRE INVENTOR TONY STARK BUILT A SUIT OF ARMOR THAT SAVED HIS LIFE. HE NOW FIGHTS AGAINST THE FORCES OF EVIL AS THE INVINCIBLE

IRON MAN

#2

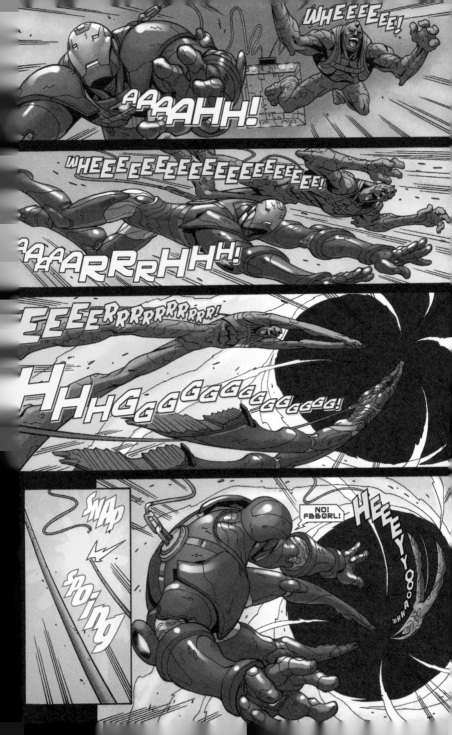

#3

#4

WHY? BECAUSE THE BANK'S "NO SHIRT, NO SHOES, NO SERVICE" POLICY MEANS THAT WE WAIT OUTSIDE WHILE IRON MAN DOES WHAT HE NEEDS TO DO, *THAT'S* WHY.

HULK DOESN'T LIKE SHIRTS.

WHICH IS *FINE.* EVERYONE'S GOT THEIR OWN IDEAS OF FASHION. I'VE GOT A FRIEND WHOSE AUNT WEARS NOTHING BUT *POLKA DOTS.*

ALWAYS POLKA DOTS. THAT'D DRIVE ME *CRAZY.*

YOU'RE KINDA *UNAFFECTED* BY THE FASHION WORLD, THOUGH, *AREN'T* YOU?

I MEAN, WHEN PANTS WITH *EXTRA POCKETS* WERE IN, *YOU* WERE STILL WEARING YOUR OLD-STYLE TORN UP *PURPLE.*

THEN BAGGY PANTS WERE ALL THE RAGE, BUT YOU STUCK WITH THE TATTERED *PURPLE.* THERE WAS THAT HORRIBLE *PATCHY BLEACH* PHASE, BUT YOU DIDN'T BUDGE.

HULK LIKES HIS PANTS.

NO PROBLEM. WORKS FOR ME. *CLASSIC HULK* IN *CLASSIC PURPLE.*

I'M JUST GLAD IT'S NOT *POLKA DOTS.* IF YOU, U ... *HEY WAIT.*

THIS POSTER... KLAW?

ISN'T HE--?

MINUTES LATER.

I NAIL THE BEETLE WITH MY **BEST PUNCH,** AND HE KEEPS GOING. BUT THE HULK JUST **LOOKS** AT HIM, AND HE SURRENDERS.

WELL, YEAH, **SURE.** IT GOES BACK TO THE "NO SHIRT, NO SHOES" FASHION SENSE. HULK JUST **LOOKS** MEAN.

HI! DARE HARRIS! CHANNEL ELEVEN! CAN I GET AN **INTERVIEW,** PLEASE?

INTERVIEW THE **HULK.** HE'S THE COOL ONE.

FORGET HOW COMPLETELY **NOT** AS COOL AS THE **HULK** YOU ARE FOR A SECOND AND TAKE A LOOK AT THIS.

REALLY? I **CAN?** THE **HULK?** WOW, THAT'S, Uhh, WOW. OKAY!

KLAW FORMED A **BAND?** THAT'S **RIDICULOUS.**

HE'S A **CRIMINAL,** RIGHT? DIDN'T I READ HE WAS A **PHYSICIST** OF SOME TYPE?

"YEAH. ULYSSES **KLAW.** MASTER OF SOUND. BUILT THE **SONIC CONVERTER** ON HIS ARM.

"IT HAS **ALL SORTS** OF POWERS, FROM FIRING **SONIC BLASTS** TO CREATING CREATURES MADE OF **PURE SOUND.**"

EVEN KLAW'S **OWN** BODY IS MADE OF SOUND.

I THINK WE BETTER GO SEE US A CONCERT.

WEIRD. SO WHY IS A **MASTER CRIMINAL** LIKE KLAW FORMING A **COUNTRY** BAND?

THIS **HAS** TO BE PART OF SOME LARGER PLAN.

Oh GOODIE. MAYBE WE'LL BUY THE HULK A BAND T-SHIRT.

HULK **DOESN'T NEED SHIRT.** HULK JUST LIKES HIS **PANTS.**

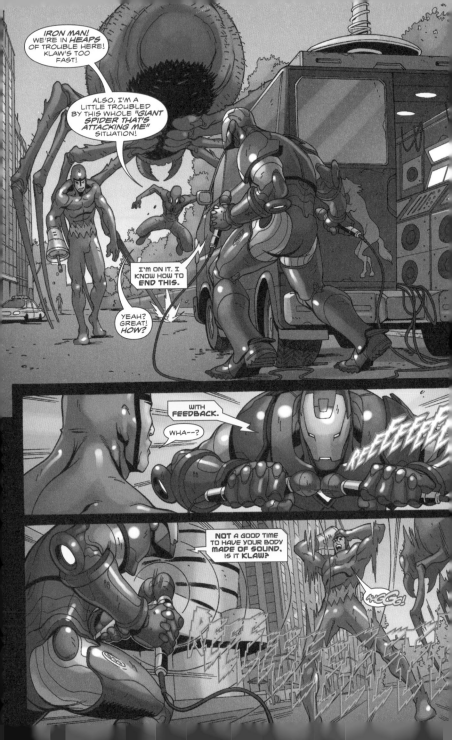